RUDOLPH
THE
RED-NOSED REINDEER®

JUMBO COLORING & ACTIVITY BOOK

©2017 The BENDON name, logo, and Tear and Share
are trademarks of Bendon, Inc., Ashland, OH 44805.

bendon®

FIND THE MISSING PIECE OF THE PUZZLE AND FINISH THE DRAWING!

1

2

3

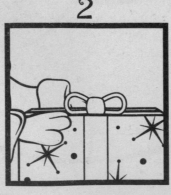

FIND THE MISSING PIECE OF THE PUZZLE AND FINISH THE DRAWING!

1

2

3

Hidden Words Search

Find and circle the words in the puzzle.
Look vertically, horizontally, and diagonally.

ELVES	TOYS
NORTH POLE	SINGING
CORNELIUS	MISFIT

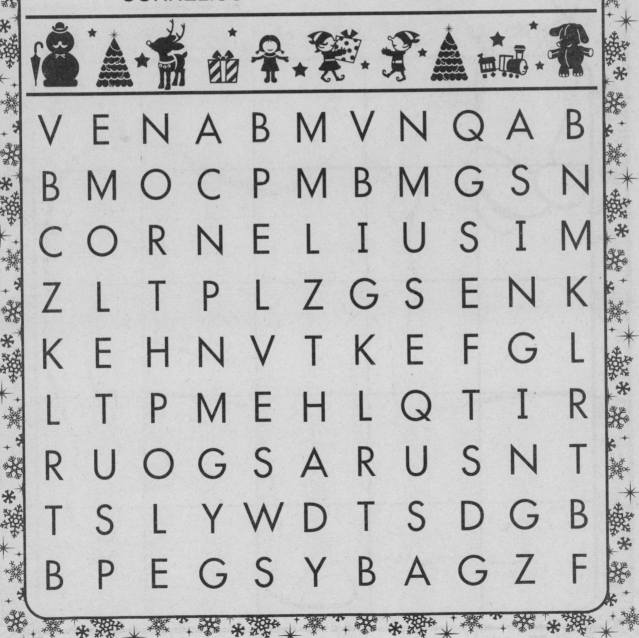

V E N A B M V N Q A B
B M O C P M B M G S N
C O R N E L I U S I M
Z L T P L Z G S E N K
K E H N V T K E F G L
L T P M E H L Q T I R
R U O G S A R U S N T
T S L Y W D T S D G B
B P E G S Y B A G Z F

You can draw!

Follow the lines in each grid to help you draw the picture below.

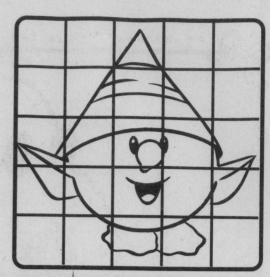

HELP HERMEY™ FIND HIS DENTAL TOOLS.

Hidden Words Search

Find and circle the words in the puzzle.
Look vertically, horizontally, and diagonally.

SNOWMAN
YUKON
PRESENT

MUSH
TREE
DECORATION

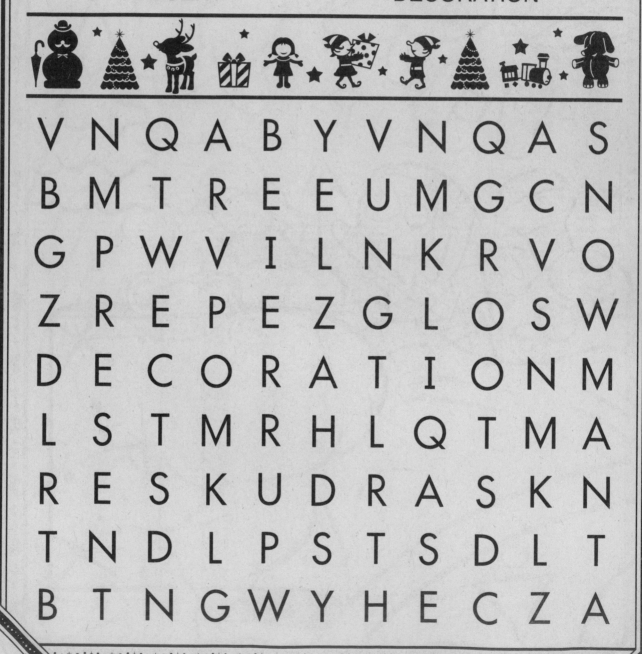

```
V N Q A B Y V N Q A S
B M T R E E U M G C N
G P W V I L N K R V O
Z R E P E Z G L O S W
D E C O R A T I O N M
L S T M R H L Q T M A
R E S K U D R A S K N
T N D L P S T S D L T
B T N G W Y H E C Z A
```

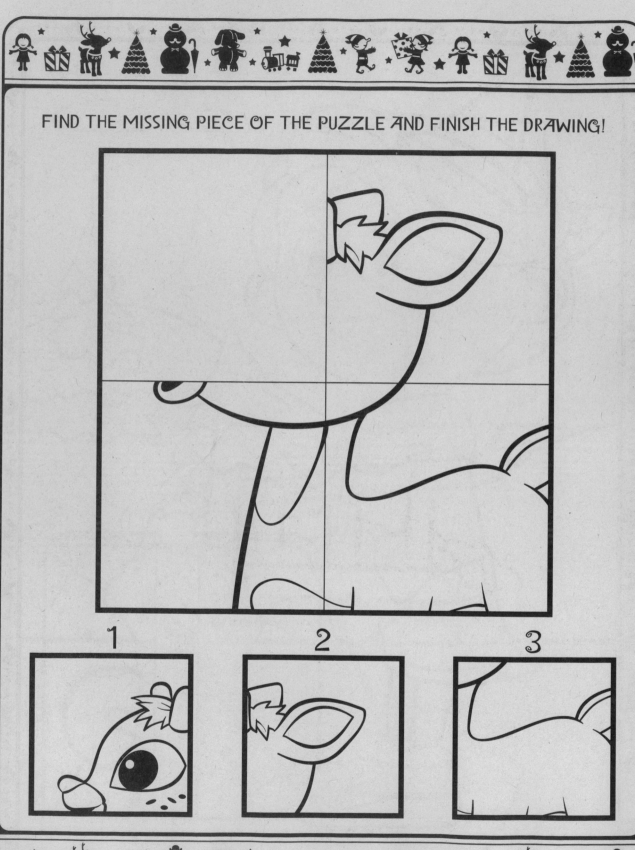

FIND THE MISSING PIECE OF THE PUZZLE AND FINISH THE DRAWING!

1   2   3

HELP THE ELF FIND THE TRAIN ENGINE.

Which picture is different?

1.

2.

3.

4.

You can draw!

Follow the lines in each grid to help you draw the picture below.

FIND THE MISSING PIECE OF THE PUZZLE AND FINISH THE DRAWING!

1   2   3

Counting

Count the images below. Circle the correct number.

4 5 6 7 8 9

HELP HERMEY™ DELIVER A GIFT TO RUDOLPH.®

Hidden Words Search

Find and circle the words in the puzzle.
Look vertically, horizontally, and diagonally.

SLEIGH	NOSE
WONDERFUL	RUDOLPH
BRIGHT	MRS. CLAUS

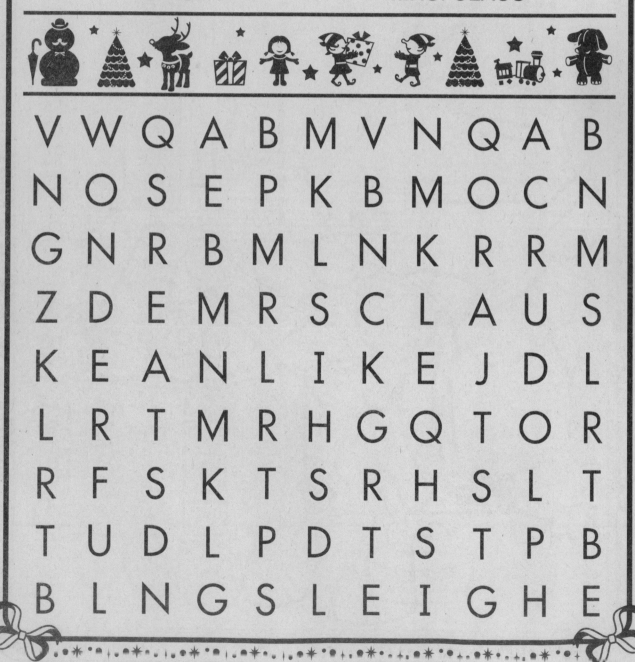

```
V W Q A B M V N Q A B
N O S E P K B M O C N
G N R B M L N K R R M
Z D E M R S C L A U S
K E A N L I K E J D L
L R T M R H G Q T O R
R F S K T S R H S L T
T U D L P D T S T P B
B L N G S L E I G H E
```

You can draw!

Follow the lines in each grid to help you draw the picture below.

HELP SANTA FIND HIS WAY THROUGH THE MAZE TO HIS SLEIGH.

Counting

Count the images below. Circle the correct number.

4 5 6 7 8 9

Which picture is different?

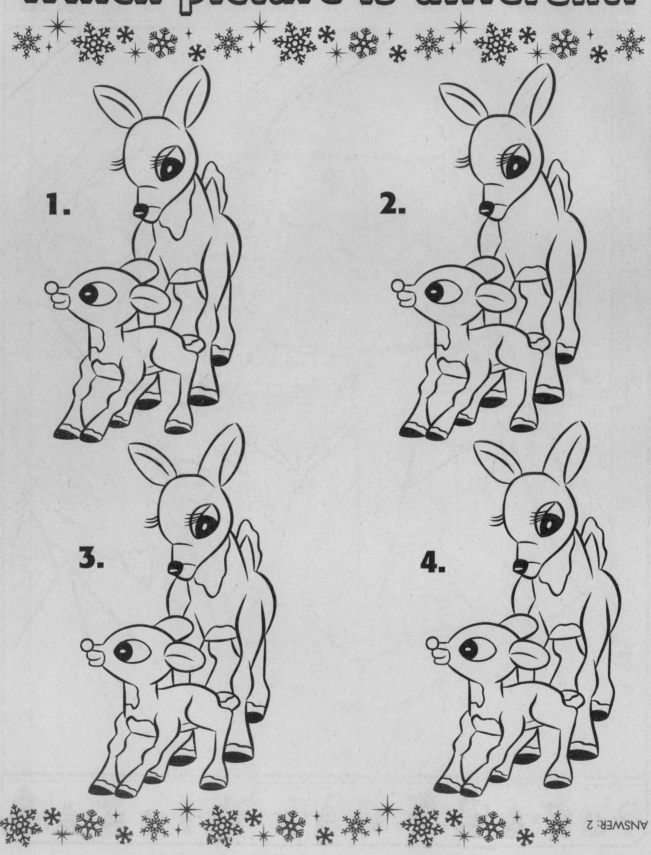

1.

2.

3.

4.

FIND THE MISSING PIECE OF THE PUZZLE AND FINISH THE DRAWING!

1

2

3

You can draw!

Follow the lines in each grid to help you draw the picture below.

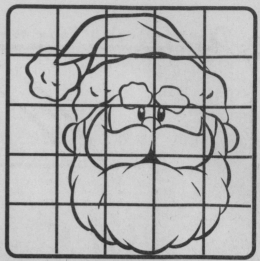

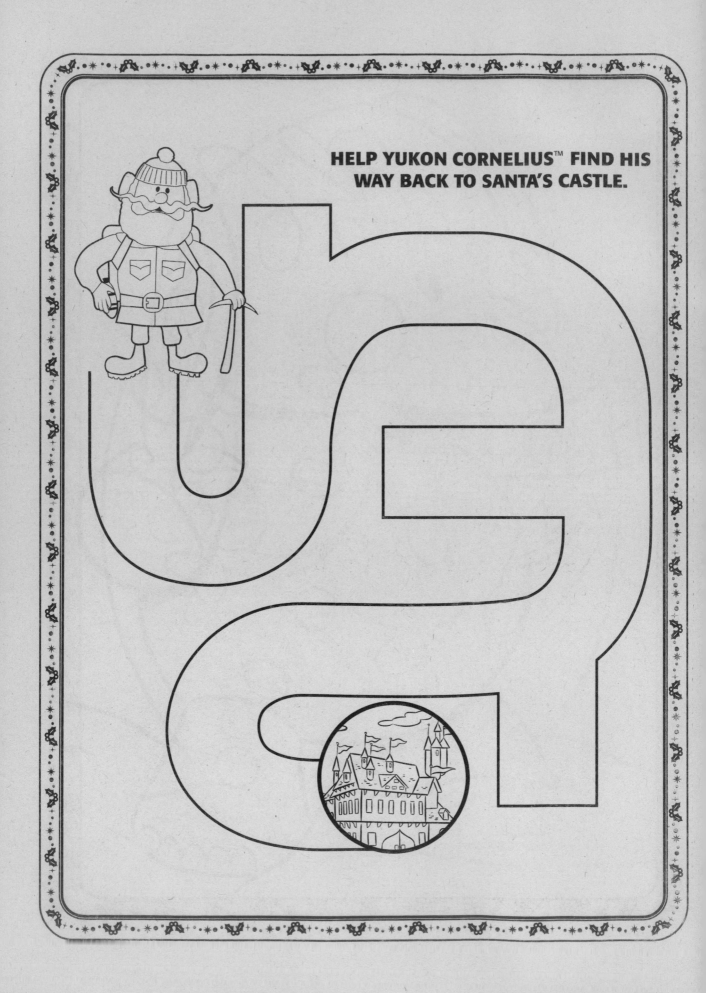

HELP YUKON CORNELIUS™ FIND HIS WAY BACK TO SANTA'S CASTLE.

Hidden Words Search

Find and circle the words in the puzzle.
Look vertically, horizontally, and diagonally.

GLOW   FRIENDS
CUTE   STOCKING
RUDOLPH   GINGERBREAD

S T O C K I N G Q A R
B M G B P F B M G C U
G I N G E R B R E A D
Z L E P E I G L E S O
K E O N L E K E A N L
L Q T W R N C Q T M P
R U S K T D R U S K H
S T C L P S T S T L B
B P N G W Y B O Z E W

Counting

Count the images below. Circle the correct number.

4 5 6 7 8 9

ANSWER: 5

FIND THE MISSING PIECE OF THE PUZZLE AND FINISH THE DRAWING!

1

2

3

HELP THE REFORMED BUMBLE™ PUT THE STAR ON THE CHRISTMAS TREE.

Which picture is different?

1.

2.

3.

4.

You can draw!

Follow the lines in each grid to help you draw the picture below.

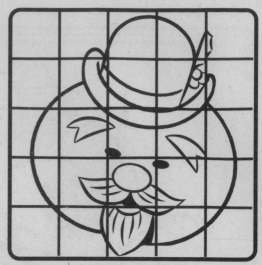

Counting

Count the images below. Circle the correct number.

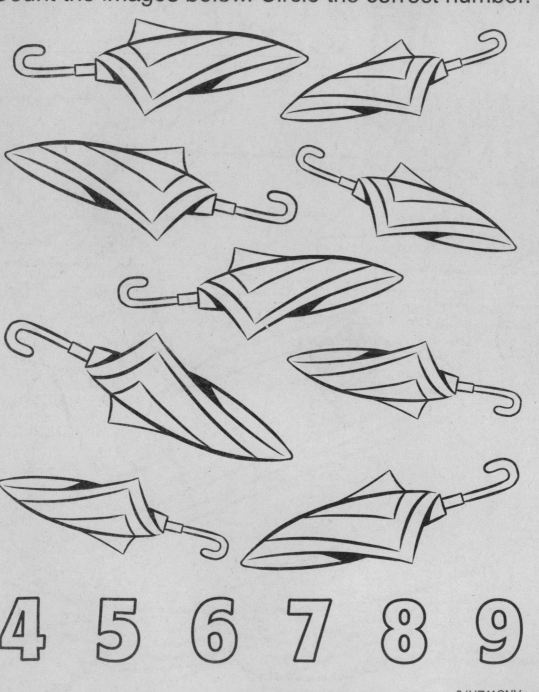

4 5 6 7 8 9

Hidden Words Search

Find and circle the words in the puzzle.
Look vertically, horizontally, and diagonally.

SANTA	REINDEER
DENTIST	SLEIGH
HERMEY	PEPPERMINT

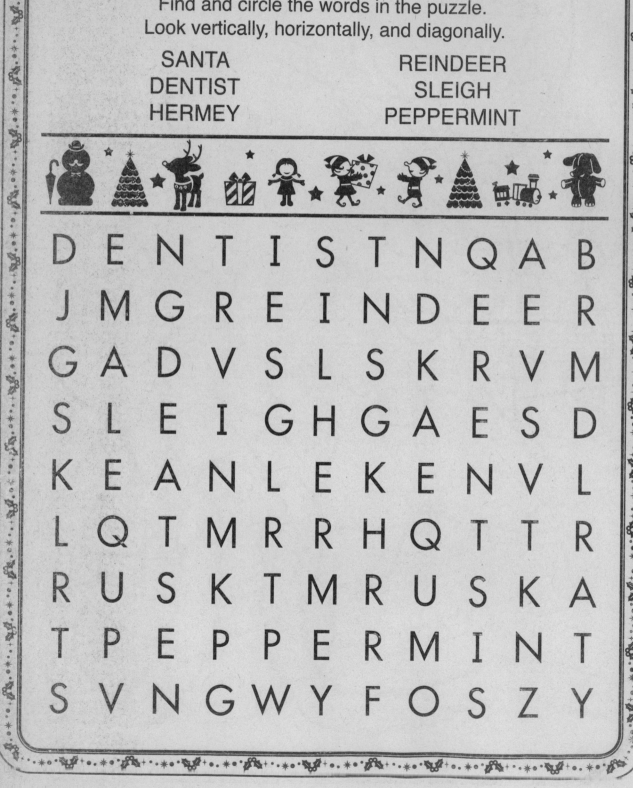

```
D E N T I S T N Q A B
J M G R E I N D E E R
G A D V S L S K R V M
S L E I G H G A E S D
K E A N L E K E N V L
L Q T M R R H Q T T R
R U S K T M R U S K A
T P E P P E R M I N T
S V N G W Y F O S Z Y
```

Which picture is different?

1.

2.

3.

4.

Counting

Count the images below. Circle the correct number.

4 5 6 7 8 9